Happy Venture Playbook

Far and Wide

FRED J. SCHONELL
and PHYLLIS FLOWERDEW

Illustrated by Bertoglio
and William Semple

OLIVER AND BOYD: EDINBURGH

Note on the Revised Edition

HAPPY VENTURE was conceived and has been validated as a basic teaching method, and as such has proved outstandingly successful. Our language is a living one, however, and so certain expressions appearing in the original edition have now gone out of use.

Before his death in 1969, Professor Schonell was actively engaged in discussion with the publishers about the revision of the entire series. Unfortunately he was not able to undertake this before he died.

After consultations with practising teachers throughout the country and abroad, it became apparent to the publishers that the principles on which the series was based had not altered, but that minor changes to up-date the text could be made without affecting the well-tested structure of the series.

Accordingly, in this book, teachers will find:

up-dating of illustrations and text where necessary, e.g. pp. 11 and 53; and consequent alterations to Word List.

The publishers acknowledge the help and advice of Miss Angela Ridsdale of Toorak Teachers' College, Malvern, Victoria, Australia, in the revision of this series.

Contents

Lunch for John

Daddy had gone to work.
Mummy had gone to the shops.
John had gone to school,
and Rags the little black dog
was all alone in the house.

"I am all alone," he thought.
"I will play a little while.
I will sleep a little while."
But then he saw something.

He saw a brown paper bag.
He looked at it. He peeped inside.
There he saw a red apple,
a big shining red apple.

"Bow-wow," thought Rags
the little black dog.
"This is John's lunch.
He has forgotten it.
I will take it to school for him."

So Rags the little black dog
picked up the brown paper bag
in his mouth
and jumped out of the window.

He walked down the garden.
He pushed open the garden gate
with his nose
and walked along the street.

He walked and he walked.
He walked and he walked.

Soon he reached John's school.
He walked up to the door,
pushed it open with his nose,
and went inside.

There he saw a green door.
It said "Class One" on it.

Rags the little black dog
pushed the door with his nose,
but it would not open.

Soon a little boy came along.
He opened the door
and went into Class One.
So Rags went in as well.

He saw children drawing.
He saw children painting,
but he did not see John.

Rags the little black dog
looked and looked and looked,
but he could not see John.
So he went out again.

Then he saw another green door.
It said " Class Two " on it.

Rags the little black dog
pushed the door with his nose,
but it would not open.

Then a little girl came along.
She opened the door
and went into Class Two.
So Rags went in as well.

He saw children dancing.
He saw children singing,
but he did not see John.

Rags the little black dog
looked and looked and looked,
but he could not see John.
So he went out again.

Then he saw another green door.
It said " Class Three " on it.

Rags the little black dog
pushed the door with his nose,
but it would not open.

Then a little boy came along.

He opened the door
and went into Class Three.
So Rags went in as well.

He saw children reading.
He saw children writing.
And there he saw John!

Then Rags the little black dog
ran to John
and dropped the brown paper bag
in front of his feet.

"Bow-wow," he said,
"here is your lunch."

John picked up the brown paper bag
and smiled.
He looked inside the bag
and saw a red apple.

"Oh, Rags has brought my lunch,"
he said. "Thank you, Rags."

The children all smiled
and patted Rags.

"Isn't he a clever dog?" they said.

Rags the little black dog
wagged his tail.
Then he went out again.

He went out of Class Three.
He went past Class Two.
He went past Class One.
Then he went
out of the school
and down the road,
and he ran
all the way home.

Dick and Dora Go on the Ferry-Boat

"It's Saturday," cried Dick
as he awoke early one morning.
"Dora, it's Saturday today,
and we are going on a ferry-boat."
He jumped up so quickly
that he fell out of bed.

This woke Dora, so she jumped
out of bed too and came in
and spoke to Dick.

"Hello, Dick," she said.
"Did you call me?"

"Yes," said Dick. "Do you know
where we are going today?"

"Oh, yes," said Dora. "I do not forget
things like that.
We are going to see Auntie May.
She has come to live in a new house
on the other side of the harbour,
so we have to catch a ferry-boat.
Won't it be fun?
I have not been on a ferry-boat before."

"It's seven o'clock," shouted Mummy.
"You must all get ready quickly."

Dick and Dora were soon ready to go
with Mummy and Daddy to the station.

"We must get a train to the river,"
said Daddy as they walked
down the road.

At the station Daddy said,
"Dick, will you please buy the tickets?"

"Yes," said Dick,
"I will get four tickets."

In the train Dick and
Dora each had a window seat,
and it was not long
before they came to the river.

When they got out of the train
Dora said,
"Dick, can you see the funnels
of the ferry-boats? They are red and
white."

As they walked down
to the ferry-boats
the sun was shining
and the sky was blue.

"It will be nice on the river today,"
said Mummy. "We shall be able to sit
on the top deck.
Now we must go through the turnstile.
Here, Dick and Dora,
 you each take a five pence piece to go
through the turnstile.
 Put the five pence piece in and push
the turnstile round."

"Click, click,"
went the turnstile, "click, click,"
as they each went through.

 There were four boats
waiting to take people up the river,
down the river, and across the river.

 They all went up the gangway
on to a ferry called the *Sea Lion*.

11

On the ferry-boat
Dick and Dora watched
the bigger boats coming and going.

There were other ferry-boats coming in
full of people. There were big, black
boats steaming out down to the sea.

There were little tugs pulling
a big boat along.
"Toot, toot," they went
if any other boat went near them.

Then the ferry-boat began to move.
"Toot, toot," it went as it steamed
slowly away,
with the sea-gulls flying above.

"What a splash the propellers make,"
shouted Dick. "Listen to the water
splashing. What a noise!"

"Yes," said Dora, "I can just hear
you speak. Look how white and silvery
the water is," she shouted back to Dick.

As they went down the river
they came alongside
a very big boat
called the *Star of India*.

STAR OF INDIA

13

On her deck were tied
a mother elephant and her baby.
They had come from India.

"Where will they be going?"
asked Dora.

"Oh, I think they must have just
come for the Zoo," said Mummy.
"If you look hard,
you can also see some monkeys
in cages on the deck."

"Toot, toot," went the ferry-boat
as it passed near to another ferry.

Just then Daddy looked up
at the Captain.

"Hullo, Bob," he cried,
"I did not see you."

"Hullo," laughed the Captain.
"What are you doing here?
Come up, and bring
the children too.

They might like to look
at the river from here."

Up to the Captain went Dick, Dora
and Daddy.

"My, my," said Captain Brown,
"it's nice to see you all."

"This is Dick," said Daddy,
"and this is Dora."

"Well," said Captain Brown,
"come and look through these windows.
You can see all the river ahead of us."

"What is that in the water?"
asked Dick.

"Oh, that's a porpoise.
He always swims ahead of every boat
when it gets here.
But he only swims on fine days.
We call him our fine-day friend.
We know that if we don't see him
it is going to rain."

15

"How quickly he can swim," said
Dora.

"Yes," said Captain Brown,
"he can swim much faster
than we can go."

Soon Captain Brown rang a bell,
and the ferry-boat began to slow down.

"We must get off here," said Daddy.

"Thank you so much, Captain,"
said Dick and Dora.
"We will look out for you
on the way back
and we will wait for the *Sea Lion*."

The Pot of Gold

Once upon a time
there was an old man
and an old woman.
They lived together in a cottage
with a red roof and a yellow door,
and they were happy
but they were very poor.

One day the old man said
to his wife,
"Last night I dreamt
that I took a spade into the garden
and dug a hole in the earth
under the apple tree.

17

I dug and I dug and I dug
and I found a pot of gold."

"Well," said the old woman,
"why don't you take a spade now,
and go into the garden
and dig a hole in the earth
under the apple tree?
Perhaps if you dig and dig
as you did in your dream
you will find a pot of gold.
Then we shall be rich."

"All right," said the old man.
"I will try."

So he took a spade into the garden
and he began to dig a hole
under the apple tree.

He dug and he dug and he dug,
and at last
his spade touched something hard.
He looked into the hole he had dug
and there he saw a stone pot.

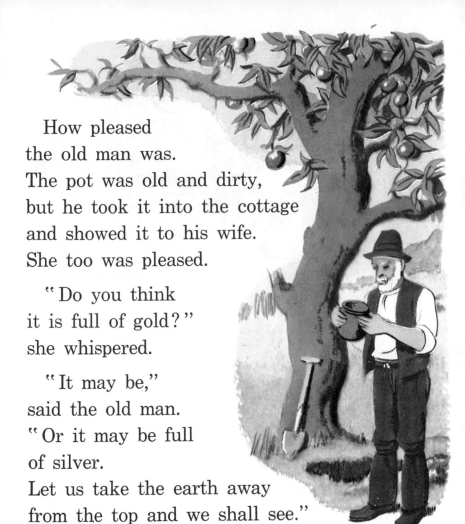

How pleased
the old man was.
The pot was old and dirty,
but he took it into the cottage
and showed it to his wife.
She too was pleased.

" Do you think
it is full of gold? "
she whispered.

" It may be,"
said the old man.
" Or it may be full
of silver.
Let us take the earth away
from the top and we shall see."

They pushed the earth
away from the top of the pot
but there was more earth beneath it.

They took that earth away
but there was more earth beneath that.

19

They took out all the earth
that was in the pot
and they found
that there was no gold,
no silver, no money.
There was nothing in the pot at all.

So the old man and the old woman
were very sad.

Then the old woman said,
"I will wash the pot and clean it well.
Then it will do for bread and milk."

So she gave the pot a good wash
and she made it clean and shining
so that it would do
for bread and milk.

Then she saw some writing on it.

"Look," said the old woman
to the old man.
"There is some writing on the pot.
Tell me what it says
for I have never been to school
and I cannot read."

"I cannot tell you,"
said the old man,
"for I have never been to school
and I cannot read."

"Oh dear," said the old woman.
"I wish I could read."

"Oh dear," said the old man.
"I wish I could read."
But they could not.

So they used the pot
for bread and milk
and they used it for many years.

Then one day a pedlar came that way.
He knocked at the door and said,
"Please, will you give me
something to eat. I am very hungry."

"Come in," said the old woman.
"We cannot give you very much
for we are poor,
but you may have
some bread and milk."

So the pedlar went
inside the cottage
and sat down at the table,
and the old woman
gave him some bread and milk.

"Thank you," said the pedlar.
"This looks very nice,
and what a fine pot it is in.
1 see there is some writing on it."

"Yes," said the old woman,
but she did not tell the pedlar
that she could not read.

"Yes," said the old man,
but he did not tell the pedlar
that he could not read.

Slowly the pedlar
turned the pot round on the table
and slowly he began to read.

The old woman listened
but she did not speak.
The old man listened
but he did not speak.

"Beneath this pot," said the pedlar,
"you will find another pot.
That is what it says."

He laughed,
and began to eat the bread and milk.

Soon he had finished.
"Thank you very much," he said,
and he walked away up the road.

The minute the pedlar had gone
the old man took the spade
and went into the garden.

He dug under the apple tree
where he had dug before,
but this time he dug deeper.

He dug deeper
and deeper
and deeper.

"Beneath this pot
you will find another pot," he said.

He dug and dug,
and at last
his spade touched something hard,
and there he saw a stone pot.

"Look," he called to his wife.
"Here is the other pot!"

The old man and the old woman
pulled the earth away
from the top of the pot
and they found
that it was full of gold,
full of shining gold.
So they were never poor again.

.   .   .   .   .

But wasn't it a good thing
that the pedlar could read?

Elephant's Afternoon Out

It was a hot afternoon in summer.
The circus people were resting
for they had come a long way
and they were tired.

They had put up their tents
in a large green field.
They had put up a cage
for the monkey
and the chimpanzee.

They had put up houses
for the seals and the kangaroo.

The ten circus horses
were sitting on the grass,
and the great grey elephant
was standing near by.

"We have done all we have to do,"
thought the circus people.
"Now we can rest till this evening."

But oh dear, what do you think
the great grey elephant did?

He swung his trunk in the air
and he thought to himself,

"I am much too hot.
I am much too hot.
I will find a pool
And make myself cool."

So he walked out of the field.
No one saw him go.

He walked along the road
and soon he came to some houses.

At the corner of the road
near the houses he saw a pond,
a small pond half-full of water.

"Just what I want,"
thought the great grey elephant.
"This will make me cool."

Slowly the great grey elephant
walked into the pond.
How nice and cool it was!

He sat down in the water
and began splashing and blowing
and playing.
He squirted water through his trunk
and he was very happy.

He became cool, cool, cool,
and cooler, cooler, cooler
till at last he became
cold, cold, cold.

"Now," thought the great
grey elephant,
"I will go back to the circus."

He tried to get out of the pond
but he could not do it,
for he found
that he was stuck in the mud.

He tried again
but still he could not do it.
He tried and he tried and he tried
but he could not get out of the pond.
He was stuck fast in the mud.

At that minute
some of the circus people
came along the road
to look for the great grey elephant.

"There he is,"
cried one of the clowns.
"Look at him.
He is stuck in the mud
and he can't get out of the pond."

By that time other people had seen
the great grey elephant too,
and the butcher, the baker, the farmer,
the shopkeeper and a lot of children
were standing near the pond.

"Look at the elephant," they shouted.
"He is stuck in the mud
and he can't get out of the pond!"

Then the circus people tried to get
the great grey elephant out of the mud.

They brought rope
and tried to pull him out with that,
but they could not move him.

They brought a car
and drove it into the pond
and tried to push him out with that,
but they could not move him.

"I know what to do,"
said the shopkeeper at last.
"There is a big crane by the river
unloading wood from a ship.
Let us ask the driver of the crane
to help us."

So one of the clowns
ran down to the river
to ask the driver of the crane
if he would help
to pull the great grey elephant
out of the pond.

"Yes," said the driver, "I will help."

So he drove the crane to the pond
and he turned it
so that it swung over the water.

Then the circus people put chains
on the great grey elephant,
and the crane pulled and pulled
and it pulled and pulled
and it pulled and pulled and pulled,
and at last
it pulled the great grey elephant
slowly, slowly out of the mud.

The crane swung him in the air
for one minute
and then it put him down
on the road on his own feet.

And that was the end
of the elephant's
afternoon out.

Wind and Fire

Once upon a time in Japan
there lived two sisters.

One was called Ching Choo
and the other was called Ching Chee.

Now Ching Choo and Ching Chee
had two brothers
who lived far, far away.
Once a year
Ching Choo and Ching Chee
said to their father,
"Father, please may we go
to see our two brothers?"

And once a year their father said,
"Your two brothers
live far, far away,
and I do not want you to leave me,
but you may go just this once."

So once a year
Ching Choo and Ching Chee
went far, far away
to see their two brothers.

Now one year
when the warm days began to come,
and the flowers grew in the grass,
and the fish swam in the pool,
Ching Choo and Ching Chee
went to their father and said,
"Father, please may we go
to see our two brothers?"

Then their father said,
"Your two brothers
live far, far away
and I do not want you to leave me,
but you may go just this once.
You may go if you will bring
two presents back for me."

"Yes, Father," said Ching Choo
and Ching Chee.
"What do you want us to bring?"

"I want two presents,"
said their father.
"I want some wind
in a piece of paper,
and I want some fire
in a piece of paper."

"Oh dear,"
said Ching Choo and Ching Chee.
"Those will be hard to find.
Can't we bring you
something better?"

"No," said their father.
"I only want some wind
in a piece of paper
and some fire in a piece of paper.
If you do not bring them for me
then you will never, never
go to see your two brothers again."

"All right," said the two sisters.
"We will bring you those things
for which you have asked."

38

So Ching Choo put on her best dress.
It was blue, with seven silver stars
painted on it.

And Ching Chee
put on her best dress.
It was red, with twelve golden flowers
painted on it.

Then they said good-bye
to their father,
and they climbed into a boat
and sailed down the river.

They lived with their two brothers
all through the summer,
and they were very happy.

One day Ching Choo
and Ching Chee
went for a walk
in the wood.

"It is so nice here,"
said Ching Choo,
"but the time
has passed quickly,
and next week
we shall have
to return home.
What are
we going to do
about the presents
for Father?"

"I do not know,"
said Ching Chee.
"I have never heard
of wind
in a piece of paper,
or fire in a piece of paper."

"No," said Ching Choo,
"neither have I."

Just then
the wind blew a piece of paper
between the trees
and dropped it
at the feet of Ching Choo.

And the voice of the wind said,
"Take the paper, Ching Choo,
and fold it this way and that,
this way and that."

41

So Ching Choo took the paper
and folded it this way and that,
this way and that.
Then she moved it up and down
in front of her face,
and she could feel the wind.

"Look," she cried.
"Here is the wind
in a piece of paper."

Just then another piece of paper
blew between the trees
and fell at the feet of Ching Chee.

And the voice of the wind said,
"Take the paper, Ching Chee,
and twist it into a ball.
Then if you put a candle inside it,
you will have fire in a piece of paper."

"So I shall," said Ching Chee.

So Ching Choo and Ching Chee
took the two presents home
to their father.

They took a fan made of paper,
and when their father held it
in front of his face
he felt wind
in a piece of paper.

They took him a lantern
made of paper and a candle,
and when their father lit it
he saw fire
in a piece of paper.

So he was very pleased
with the two sisters.

And that,
so the people of Japan say,
is the story of the first fan
and the first lantern.

The New King

Once England had no king.
The old king had gone,
and there was no one
to take his place.

"We must have a king,"
said the people.
"Whom shall we have?"

But some people
asked for a strong man
and some asked for a wise man.
Some asked for an old man
and some asked for a young man.

So the days went by
and the people did not know
whom to have for king.

Then one morning
they found a sword.

It was long and shining.
It was sharp and bright,
and it was stuck in a great stone.

No one knew where it came from.
No one knew how it had come.
But there it was, long and shining,
sharp and bright.

And on the stone were these words,
    "He who pulls
      this sword
    from the stone
    shall be king."

So the people
called their strongest men.
"You try to pull out the sword,"
they said.

One by one the strong men tried.
One by one they pulled and pulled
at the sword,
but the sword was stuck fast
in the stone.
Not one of the strong men
could move it.

Then the people
called their wisest men.
"You try to pull out
the sword,"
they said.

One by one the wise men tried.
One by one they pulled and pulled
at the sword,
but the sword was stuck fast
in the stone.
Not one of the wise men
could move it.

Then the people called
their oldest men.
"You try to pull out the sword,"
they said.

One by one the old men tried.
One by one they pulled and pulled
at the sword,
but the sword was stuck fast
in the stone.
Not one of the old men could move it.

Then the people
called their youngest men.
"You try to pull out the sword,"
they said.

One by one the young men tried.
One by one they pulled and pulled
at the sword,
but the sword was stuck fast
in the stone.
Not one of the young men
could move it.

So there was the sword,
long and shining, sharp and bright,
and it was still stuck
in the great stone.

The strong men could not move it.
The wise men could not move it.
The old men could not move it.
The young men could not move it.

Then the people
read the words again.

" He who pulls
this sword
from the stone
shall be king."

"Let others try," they said.

So one by one others tried.

Those who were not so strong tried, but they could not move the sword.

Those who were not so wise tried, but they could not move the sword.

Those who were not so old tried, but they could not move the sword.

Those who were not so young tried, but they could not move the sword.

Then came a boy named Arthur.
He put his foot on the great stone.
He took hold of the great sword
with his two hands.
He gave one pull,
and out came the sword,
long and shining,
sharp and bright.

The people gave
a loud cheer.

"Arthur is our king!"
they cried.
"Arthur is our king!"

So Arthur was made
king of England,
and he grew up
to be strong and wise
and brave and good.

The Lost Bone

Early one morning a dog found a bone.
It was a very small bone
but it had some meat on it.

The dog picked it up in his mouth
and walked across a field with it.

Now in this field was an old mine,
a deep, dark mine,
where men had dug for tin.
Most of the tin had been dug up,
and the mine was not used now,
but there was still a great hole
left in the earth.

The dog walked along
with the bone in his mouth.

Then he stopped
to look down the old mine,
down the deep, dark mine.

He saw the great hole in the earth,
where men had dug for tin,
but while he was looking,
he dropped his bone
and it fell down, down the mine,
down the deep, dark mine.

"Oh dear," thought the dog,
"I have lost my bone.
It was a very small one
but it had some good meat on it."

The dog was hungry
and he wanted the bone,
so he kept running up and down
near the old mine.

Soon some men came along
on their way to work.
"Hullo," they said to the dog.
"What do you want?"

They patted him,
and he wagged his tail
but he still kept running
up and down
near the old mine,
for he wanted
his bone.

In the afternoon
some children passed the mine.

They saw the dog
running up and down.

They spoke to him and called him
and tried to make him come away,
but he would not leave the mine.

In the evening some people came
from the houses near by
and gave the dog
something to eat.

They spoke to him
and called him
and tried to make
him come away,
but he would not
leave the mine,
for he wanted
his bone.

Then night came.
It was dark and cold
and it rained,
but still the dog
would not leave the mine.

Next morning
when the people awoke
in the houses near by
they ran to the old mine
to see if the dog was still there.

Yes, there he was,
still running up and down.

"He has been there
twenty-four hours," said a boy.
"A day and a night," said a girl.

Then a woman said, "Perhaps someone
has fallen down the old mine.
Perhaps the dog's master
has fallen down."

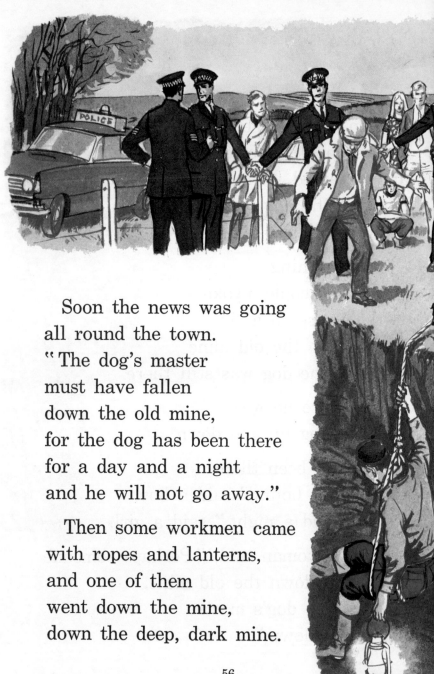

Soon the news was going
all round the town.
" The dog's master
must have fallen
down the old mine,
for the dog has been there
for a day and a night
and he will not go away."

Then some workmen came
with ropes and lanterns,
and one of them
went down the mine,
down the deep, dark mine.

Lots of people came to watch,
and the dog looked pleased
and began to bark.
Down, down, down went the workman,
swinging on the rope
and holding the lantern.

Then after a long while
he came up to the top again.

"I could not go right down," he said,
"for the mine is half-full of water."

"Oh dear," said the people
to one another.
"Just think of the poor man
lying down there waiting for help.
We shall have
to pump the water away."

"Bow-wow," barked the dog,
and he kept running
up and down near the mine,
for he wanted his bone.

Then some workmen came
with a great pump
and they pumped and pumped
for hours and hours and hours.

By this time thousands
of people had come
to watch.

Some walked to the place.
Others came by bus or drove up in cars.

They brought bread and meat
and milk for the dog,
and they stood around the old mine
and watched the workmen.
They watched them
pump the water away
for hours and hours and hours.

At four o'clock in the afternoon
one of the workmen said,
"We have finished
pumping the water away.
Now we must look
for the dog's master."

So the workmen
went swinging down on ropes
and holding lanterns.

They went down the deep, dark mine,
and they looked and they looked
everywhere, everywhere, everywhere.

And what did they find?
Did they find the dog's master?
No.

Did they find a man who had fallen
down the deep, dark mine?
No.

Did they find a woman
or a boy or a girl?
No.

They found only a bone,
a very small bone.

When they brought the bone
to the top of the old mine,
they held it up for the people to see.
And the thousands of people
laughed and laughed,
but the little dog wagged his tail
and said, "Bow-wow,
that is just what I wanted."

The Goldfish

One day Richard and Granddad
went to the fair.

They listened to the music
of the merry-go-round.
They watched the children,
swinging in the swing boats.

Then they heard a man shouting,
" Who wants to win a goldfish ?
Seven balls for five pence!"

" Oh," said Richard to Granddad,
" I should like to win a goldfish."

" Let us go and watch first,"
said Granddad.

So Richard and Granddad
went towards the stand
where the man shouted,
" Who wants to win a goldfish ?
Seven balls for five pence!"

On the stand they saw lots of jars
with goldfish swimming in them.
The jars had very small tops,
and the balls were very light.

Just then a big boy came along.

" Who wants to win a goldfish ? "
shouted the man again.
"Seven balls for five pence!"

" I will have a try,"
said the big boy,
and he gave the man five pence.

"Here are the balls," said the man.
"If you get one on top of a jar,
I will give you a goldfish."

He gave the boy seven balls,
and the big boy began to throw.
He threw one, two, three,
four, five, six, seven balls.
But every ball missed the jars,
so the boy did not get a goldfish.

He laughed and walked away.

Just then a woman came along.

"Who wants to win a goldfish?"
shouted the man again.
"Seven balls for five pence!"

"I will have a try,"
said the woman,
and she gave the man five pence.

"Here are the balls," said the man.
"If you get one on top of a jar,
I will give you a goldfish."

He gave the woman seven balls,
and the woman began to throw.
She threw one, two, three, four,
five, six, seven balls.
But every ball missed the jars,
so the woman did not get a goldfish.

She laughed and walked away.

Then Grandfather said to Richard,
" Would you like to try ? "

" Yes please," said Richard.
" I should like to try,
for I might win a goldfish."

So Granddad put five pence into the
man's hand,
and the man gave seven balls
to Richard.

"Thank you," said Richard,
and he began to throw.

He threw the first ball. It missed.
He threw the second and third balls.
They missed.
He threw the fourth
and the fifth
and the sixth balls.
They missed.

"Only one left now," said Richard.
"I *do* want to win a goldfish."

Then he threw the seventh ball.
It sailed through the air
above the jars on the stand.
Then it dropped down.

It dropped on to a jar
with a soft little tap.
Then it bounced off again.

"Oh," said Richard.
"I thought I had won."

"I thought so too,"
said Grandfather.

But the man at the stand said,
"You may take that ball again,"
and he passed it back to Richard.

So Richard took the seventh ball
and threw it once more,
and it dropped on to a jar again.
And this time it stayed there.

"Oh look!" cried Richard.
"It is on a jar this time."

"Yes," said the man at the stand.
"You have done well."
He picked up the jar
with a goldfish swimming inside,
and he gave it to Richard.

"Thank you," said Richard,
and he was very pleased.

Then Grandfather said,
"Don't you think it would be nice
to go to the pet shop
and buy a brother for the goldfish?"

"Oh, yes," said Richard,
"that would be very nice."

So Richard and Grandfather
left the fair and went to the pet shop.

There Grandfather bought
a better jar and another goldfish
and some green water weed
and some goldfish food.

" Oh," cried Richard,
" what a lot of things
you have bought for me.
You are a very kind Grandfather."

So now there are two goldfish
swimming in a jar
in a room in Richard's house.
They swim in and out
of the green water weed
and they eat the goldfish food
that Richard puts in for them
every day.

Eskimo Puppy

Far away, in the land of the Eskimos,
there was a little round house.
The walls and the roof
were made of snow,
and the windows were made of ice.

In the little round house
lived an Eskimo father
and an Eskimo mother,
an Eskimo boy and an Eskimo girl,
and a small fat Eskimo baby.

The baby was dressed in fur
from the top of his head
to the tip of his toes,
so that he looked
more like a snowball than a baby.

Outside the little round house
lived the Eskimo dogs,
eight great big Eskimo dogs,
and one little fat Eskimo puppy.

The puppy had a white fur coat
from the top of his head
to the tip of his paws,
so that he looked
more like a snowball than a puppy.

The big dogs never went
inside the little round house.
They played in the snow in the day time
and slept in the snow at night.

But the little fat puppy
went in and out of the house
as he wished.

He played with the children
in the day time
and slept by the fire at night.

Sometimes the Eskimo people
went for a ride on their sledge.
The eight great big dogs
would pull the sledge
over the snow, over the snow,
over the shining white snow.

But the little fat puppy
would ride on the sledge
with the Eskimo father and mother
and the Eskimo boy and girl
and the small fat Eskimo baby.

He would look for white bears
on the ice.

He would look for black sea lions
in the snow,
and when he was tired of looking,
he would curl up
with the small fat Eskimo baby
and go to sleep.

One day the Eskimo father said,
"The sun is bright,
and the snow is shining.
We will go for a ride
on the sledge."

So the Eskimo father and mother
and the Eskimo boy and girl
and the small fat Eskimo baby
all went on the sledge.

The little fat Eskimo puppy
jumped up with them,
and the eight great big dogs
pulled the sledge
over the snow, over the snow,
over the shining white snow.

The Eskimo boy
and the Eskimo girl
and the little fat Eskimo puppy
looked for white bears on the ice.
They looked for black sea lions
in the snow.

But the small fat Eskimo baby
curled up in the back of the sledge
and went to sleep.

He was dressed in fur
from the top of his head
to the tip of his toes,
so that he looked
more like a snowball than a baby.

The eight great big dogs
pulled the sledge
over the snow, over the snow,
over the shining white snow.

Then they came to a place
where the sledge went
bump, bump, bump, bump!

At first the bumps were small,
but soon there was a very big one.

It was so big
that the sledge went
BUMP,
and the small fat Eskimo baby
bounced right up in the air
and rolled into the snow.

The Eskimo mother and father
did not look behind them,
so they did not know
that the baby had fallen.

The Eskimo boy and the Eskimo girl
did not look behind them,
so they did not know
that the baby had fallen.

But the little fat Eskimo puppy
saw the small fat Eskimo baby
bounce right off the sledge
and roll into the snow.

Quickly the puppy jumped!
He jumped off the sledge
and ran and ran
to the small fat Eskimo baby
who was still fast asleep.

The Eskimo father and mother
did not look behind them,
so they did not know
that the puppy had gone.

The Eskimo boy and the Eskimo girl
did not look behind them,
so they did not know
that the puppy had gone.

The sledge went on and on
over the snow, over the snow,
over the shining white snow.

After a long while
the Eskimo mother looked round.
"Oh!" she cried. "Where is Baby?
And where is the puppy?"

Father stopped the sledge at once.
He jumped down into the snow
and looked all round,
but he could not find the baby,
and he could not find the puppy.

Mother and the children looked too,
but they could not find the baby
or the puppy.

Then the Eskimo mother said,
"We must go back the way we came."

So they got on to the sledge
once more,
and the eight great big dogs
turned it round and pulled it back
the way they had come.

They pulled it back
over the snow, over the snow,
over the shining white snow.

As they drove along,
the Eskimo mother and father looked,
and the Eskimo boy and girl looked,
but they could not see the baby,
and they could not see the puppy.

Then at last the Eskimo boy
heard a noise.

"Listen," he said.
"I can hear a dog barking."

Father stopped the sledge
and everyone sat still and listened.

They heard a dog barking,
"Bow-wow, bow-wow, bow-wow!"

"It must be the puppy," they said.

They jumped down from the sledge
and looked all round.

There in the snow
they saw the small fat Eskimo baby
curled up asleep,
looking more like a snowball
than a baby.

And they saw
the little fat Eskimo puppy
sitting up by the baby
and looking very proud
of himself.

"You good dog!" cried Mother,
and she picked up the baby.

"You good dog!" cried Father
and the children.

They patted
the small fat Eskimo puppy,
and he wagged his tail.

Then everyone went back
on to the sledge.

The Eskimo mother
held the small fat Eskimo baby.
The Eskimo children
held the little fat Eskimo puppy,
and they all drove home once more.

The eight great big dogs
pulled the sledge
over the snow, over the snow,
over the shining white snow.

At last they came
to the little
round house
with the walls
and the roof
made of snow
and the windows
made of ice.

Johnnie Appleseed

Once there lived an old man
who was called Johnnie Appleseed.
He was very poor.
His clothes were in rags,
and he had a saucepan for a hat.

He lived in America, in a place
where there were no white people.
He did not want to live in a house,
for he liked to walk over the hills
and through the fields
and in the deep, dark woods.

He liked to drink
from the cool rivers
and sleep at night
under the shining stars.

One day when he was walking,
Johnnie Appleseed thought,
" These fields and woods
are very beautiful.

" Some day other people will find them.

They will come here
and make houses and farms.
They will come here to live
and to work.

"I know what I will do.
I will plant some apple seeds.

"The apple seeds will grow
into little trees,
and by the time people come
to live here
the apple trees will be big."

So Johnnie Appleseed
walked back to a place
where people had already
made houses and farms,
and he said to a farmer,
"Please, will you give me
some apple seeds?"

"Yes," said the farmer.
"We have such a lot of apples
that many of them
are lying on the ground going bad
under the trees.
You may take as many as you wish."

So Johnnie Appleseed
cut out the seeds
from hundreds of apples
and put the seeds
in an old bag.

Then he went to another farmer.
"Please, will you give me
some apple seeds?" he said.

"Yes," said the second farmer.
"We have such a lot of apples
that many of them
are lying on the ground going bad
under the trees.
You may take as many as you wish."

So Johnnie Appleseed
cut out the seeds
from hundreds more apples,
and he put the seeds in his bag.

He went from farm to farm
asking for apple seeds
all through the summer.

He took hundreds
and hundreds of seeds from apples
that no one wanted.

Then at last, when his bag was full,
he walked back
to the fields and the woods
where no one lived.

He dug small holes in the earth
and planted apple seeds.
He spread the soil over the seeds
and left them there to grow.

Then he walked a little way
and planted more seeds.

He spread the soil over them
and left them there to grow.

Johnnie Appleseed
went on planting apple seeds
for weeks and weeks and weeks.

He planted them on the hills
and in the fields
and in the deep, dark woods.
Everywhere he went
he planted apple seeds.

The sun shone and the rain fell,
and soon the seeds began to grow.

They grew and grew
till they were little trees.
Then they grew and grew
till they were big trees
with fine green leaves
and red and golden apples.

Then at last, years after,
some people came that way.

" These fields and woods
are very beautiful," they said.
"We will make houses and farms here.
We will live and work here."

And then, oh what a surprise!

They found some apple trees,
tall and beautiful,
with fine green leaves
and red and golden apples.

"Oh, how nice!" they cried.
"Johnnie Appleseed
must have planted them."

For by that time
many people knew Johnnie Appleseed,
and many people loved him.

Then more people came that way.
"These fields and woods
are very beautiful," they said.

"We will make houses and farms here.
We will live and work here."

Then they too had a surprise.
They found some apple trees,
big and beautiful,
with fine green leaves
and red and golden apples.

"Oh, how nice!" they cried.
"Johnnie Appleseed .
must have planted them for us."

And all over that part of America
people began to find
Johnnie Appleseed's apple trees
ready and waiting for them.

Johnnie Appleseed grew older,
and his clothes grew older,
and his saucepan hat grew older,
but he went on walking
over the hills
and through the fields
and in the deep, dark woods.

He went on drinking
from the cool rivers
and sleeping at night
under the shining stars,
and he went on
for years
and years and years
planting apple trees,
planting apple trees
for other people
to find.

Bobby the Budgie

When Sandra was six years old
there were lots of presents
for her.

There was a doll and a ball,
a book and a sugar pig,
and there was something else,
something very large,
done up in brown paper.

"What can it be?" said Sandra.

She cut the string
and pulled off the brown paper.

"Oh, what a beautiful present!"
she cried,
for there was a silver cage,
and inside it
was a little bird
with green
and yellow feathers
as soft as thistledown.

"Oh!" cried Sandra.
"Isn't he nice?
What kind of a bird
is he, Mummy?"

"He's a budgie," said Mummy.

"And he can speak," said Daddy.
"He can say,
'Humpty Dumpty sat on a wall.'"

"Can he?" said Sandra,
and she laughed.

"I shall call him Bobby," she said,
holding her hand up
to the silver wires of the cage.
"I shall call him Bobby the budgie."

So Bobby the budgie
lived with Sandra
and her mother and father.

Often in the evenings
Sandra would open the cage door,
and Bobby would hop right out
and fly round the room.

He would even come down
and sit on her hand,
and sometimes, just sometimes,
he would say in a funny little voice,
"Humpty Dumpty sat on a wall."

One day Sandra thought
she would teach him to say his name,
so she stood in front of the silver cage
and she said,
"Say 'My name is Bobby.'"

But Bobby the budgie
only shook himself and said,
"Humpty Dumpty sat on a wall."

"No," said Sandra.
"Say 'My name is Bobby.'"

But Bobby the budgie
only shook himself and said,
"Humpty Dumpty sat on a wall."

"No," said Sandra again.
"Say 'My name is Bobby.'"

But Bobby the budgie
only shook himself once more
and said in his funny little voice,
"Humpty Dumpty sat on a wall."

Sandra tried and tried
for many evenings,
but she could not make
Bobby the budgie say his name.

Then at last one evening she stood
in front of the silver cage and she said,
"Say 'My name is Bobby.'"

And this time Bobby the budgie
shook his green and yellow feathers
and said in a funny little voice,
"My name is Bobby.
Humpty Dumpty sat on a wall."

Sandra was very glad.
"Now I will teach you
where you live," she said.
"Say 'My name is Bobby.
I live at twenty-eight King's Road.'"

But Bobby the budgie
only shook himself and said,
"My name is Bobby.
Humpty Dumpty sat on a wall."

"No," said Sandra.
"Say 'My name is Bobby.
I live at twenty-eight King's Road.'"

But Bobby the budgie
only shook himself and said,
"My name is Bobby.
Humpty Dumpty sat on a wall."

"No," said Sandra again.
"Say 'My name is Bobby.
I live at twenty-eight King's Road.'"

But Bobby the budgie
only shook himself once more
and said in his funny little voice,
"My name is Bobby.
Humpty Dumpty sat on a wall."

Sandra tried and tried
for many evenings,
but she could not make
Bobby the budgie say
where he lived.

Then at last one evening she stood
in front of the silver cage
and she said,
" Say ' My name is Bobby.
I live at twenty-eight King's Road.' "

And this time Bobby the budgie
shook his green and yellow feathers
as soft as thistledown,
and said in a funny little voice,
" My name is Bobby.
I live at twenty-eight King's Road.
Humpty Dumpty sat on a wall."

" Oh, you clever little bird,"
cried Sandra, and she called out,
" Mummy, Bobby knows his name
and where he lives.
Do come and listen to him."

Days and weeks went by,
and Bobby the budgie
was very happy
with Sandra.

Then one night
someone left open
the door of the cage,
and someone left open
a window in the room,
and when Sandra came down
the next morning
to say "Hallo" to Bobby,
Bobby was not there.

He had flown away in the night.

"Oh!" cried Sandra. "He has gone!"

Daddy took her out at once
to look for him.
They looked over all the fences
and up in all the trees,
but they could not find Bobby.

" Perhaps he will come back soon,"
said Daddy. But he did not.
He did not come back all day.

The days went by,
one, two, three, four, five, six,
and still Bobby did not come back.
Sandra was very sad.

Then on the seventh day
an old woman knocked at the door.
She held a small box in her hands,
and she said,
" Have you lost a budgie ? "

" Oh, yes ! " said Sandra and Mummy.

They took the old woman
into the house.

She opened the box,
and out flew Bobby the budgie.
He went right up to the cage
and jumped inside.

"You see," said the old woman,
"I live a long way off
at the other side of the town.

"Last week this little bird
flew into my house.
I looked after him
and tried to make him speak.
For three days he said nothing.

"Then on the fourth day he said,
'Humpty Dumpty sat on a wall.'
On the fifth day he said,
'My name is Bobby,'
and on the sixth day he said,
'I live at twenty-eight King's Road.'
So then I knew where to bring him."

"Oh, thank you," said Sandra.
"I am so pleased to have him back.

What a good thing
I was able to teach him
his name and where he lived."

She stood in front of the cage
and held up her hand
to the silver wires,
and Bobby the budgie
shook his green and yellow feathers
as soft as thistledown,
and he said,
"My name is Bobby.
I live at twenty-eight King's Road.
Humpty Dumpty sat on a wall."

A Ride on a Bus

Rags the little black dog
went walking down the road,
wagging his tail from side to side.
Soon he came to a bus stop
where a lot of people
were waiting for a bus.

Now Rags had always wanted
to ride on a bus,
and he thought to himself,
"Today I will have a ride."

So he stood at the bus stop
with all the people.
He waited and he waited.

Soon the bus came.
It stopped at the bus stop,
and the people went on to it.

Some went up the stairs,
some went inside,
and the conductor shouted,
" Hurry along, please."

On jumped Rags.
He ran up the stairs
and sat down
at the front.

The conductor
rang the bell,
and the bus started
on its way.

" This is nice,"
thought Rags.

"I will have a long ride,
all the way to town and back again."

But soon the conductor
came upstairs shouting,
"Fares, please! Fares, please!"

He saw Rags at the front.

He looked at all the men
reading their papers
and he said,
"Is this your little black dog?"

All the men
looked over their papers and said,
"No, he isn't mine."

Then the conductor looked
at all the ladies
holding their shopping baskets
and he said,
"Is this your little black dog?"

All the ladies looked
over their shopping baskets
and said, "No, he isn't mine."

Then the conductor
looked at the children
riding on the bus to school
and he said,
"Is this your little black dog?"

The children laughed and said,
"No, he isn't mine."

So then the conductor
looked at Rags and said,
"You will have to get off the bus."
He took Rags down the stairs,
and when the bus stopped
at the next stop
he put him down on to the road.

The bus went on its way,
but Rags was very sad.
His bus ride had been
so short.

Now the next morning
Rags went walking down the road,
wagging his tail from side to side.
Soon he came to the bus stop
where a lot of people
were waiting for the bus.

Rags wanted a ride so much,
and he thought to himself,
"I will try again today."

He stood at the bus stop
with all the people
and waited for the bus.
He waited and waited.

Soon the bus came.
It stopped at the bus stop,
and the people went on to it.

Some went upstairs,
some went inside,
and the conductor shouted,
" Hurry along, please."

On jumped Rags.
He ran up the stairs quickly
but this time he crept under a seat
at the front, and he kept so still
that no one knew he was there.

The conductor rang the bell,
and the bus started on its way.

The conductor
went upstairs shouting,
"Fares, please! Fares, please!"
But he did not see Rags.

So the bus went on and on,
and Rags went on and on with it.

Soon the bus came to the school.
The children ran down the stairs,
jumped off the bus,
and ran into the school.
But Rags lay
under the seat
and went on
with the bus.

Soon the bus came to the shops.
The ladies with their shopping baskets
went down the stairs,
jumped off the bus,
and went into the shops.
But Rags lay under the seat
and went on with the bus.

Soon the bus came to the offices.
The men folded their papers,
ran down the stairs, jumped off the bus,
and went into the offices.
But Rags lay under the seat
and went on with the bus.

Then he saw that there was
no one left on top of the bus at all.
"Good!" he thought.
"Now I can stand up."

He crept out from under the seat,
and he stood up.

At that very minute
the conductor came upstairs!

"Well!"
he said.
"This is
the second day
you have been
on my bus!"

Rags went up
to the conductor,
wagging his tail
from side to side.

"You are
a very nice little dog,"
said the conductor slowly.
"There is no one on the bus,
so perhaps I will let you
finish your ride today."

So Rags stood at the front of the bus
and rode all the way to town
and all the way back,
and he was as happy as could be.

White Fur Gloves

There was once a little girl
called Jill,
who had a pair of white fur gloves.

One afternoon when she was out
with her mother,
her mother said,
" Oh, I have a letter to post.
There is a pillar box.
Post the letter for me, please."

Jill took the letter,
ran to the pillar box,
and pushed the letter into it.

She pushed so hard
that her hand went in a little way,
and when she pulled it out again
she had lost her white fur glove.

She had posted it in the pillar box
with the letter!

" Oh dear ! " said Jill,
and she went back to her mother.

Mummy did not see
that Jill had lost a glove,
but after a while Jill said,
" Mummy, where do the letters
in the pillar box go ? "

" The postman puts them in his bag
and takes them to the post office
to be sorted," said Mummy.

" What would the postman do
if he found something else
in the box ? " asked Jill.

" Well," said Mummy,
" he might think someone had
put it in as a present for him."

Then Jill said,
" What would
the postman do
if he found a glove
with the letters,
—a white fur glove? "

Then Mummy
looked at
Jill's hands,
one with a glove,
and one without,
and she said,
" Oh Jill,
did you post your glove ? "

" It caught in the hole," said Jill,
" and it slid down inside."

" Oh," said Mummy.
" They are such nice fur gloves.
I will write a letter to the postman
and put it in the pillar box.
Then perhaps when he takes the letters
he will send the glove back to us."

So Mummy wrote a letter
and put it in the pillar box.

The next day Jill thought
the white fur glove might come back.

But a letter came for Daddy
and a letter came for Mummy,
but no white fur glove came for Jill.

The day after that Jill thought
the white fur glove might come back.

But two letters came for Daddy
and two letters came for Mummy,
but no white fur glove came for Jill.

Then a week passed by,
and Mummy said,
" We must forget about the glove, Jill.
I don't think it will come back now."

So one little white fur glove
was left lying in the house.

Then two weeks passed by,
and Mummy said,
" It is no good keeping
one white fur glove, Jill.
Put it in the dustbin."

Sadly Jill took the white fur glove
and dropped it into the dustbin.
"And that is the end of that,"
she thought.

But it was not.

The next morning
the dustmen came down the road.

They took the dustbins.
They shouted and sang
and put the dust into the cart.

At the same time,
at the very same time,
a postman came down the road too.

He had lots of letters in his bag,
and he had something else.
He had the little white fur glove
that Jill had posted two weeks before.

Along came the dustmen.

They opened Jill's gate.
They took her dustbin,
with one white fur glove inside,
and they put the dust
and the white fur glove into their cart.

Then along came the postman.

He knocked at Jill's door,
and when Mummy and Jill opened it
he said, " Is this the white fur glove
you posted the week before last ? "

" Oh yes ! " cried Jill.

" Thank you," said Mummy.

Then they looked at each other
and said,
" The other one was in the dustbin,
and the dustmen have just been."

" Quick, Jill," said Mummy.
"Run and ask them
if they can find it."

Out ran Jill
down the road to the dustcart.

"Please," she said to the dustman,
" could you find
my white fur glove?
It was in the dustbin."

One of the dustmen
stopped singing
and opened
one of the doors
at the side of the cart,
and there,
right in front,
was the glove.

"Well, you are lucky,"
said the dustman.

He shook some dust
and tea leaves
from the white fur glove
and gave it to Jill.

"Thank you," said Jill.

She ran back home,
where Mummy
and the postman
were still waiting
at the door.

"Here it is,"
shouted Jill,
and the postman said,
just as the dustman
had said,
"Well, you are lucky."

Word List

This list shows all the new words (117) in Playbook 4 other than straight-forward derivatives from words already known (e.g. pleased); more difficult derivatives, such as 'someone', are listed. All the remaining words in the book have already occurred in Book 4 or in the earlier stages of the Happy Venture reading scheme. The numbers refer to the pages on which the words first appear.

2 class	16 rang	39 golden
3 drawing	17 dreamt	41 voice
6 writing	dug	fold
patted	18 perhaps	42 face
7 isn't	19 beneath	twist
wagged	20 nothing	candle
8 ferry	22 used	43 felt
awoke	pedlar	lantern
woke	23 turned	44 king
spoke	25 deeper	England
9 forget	26 wasn't	whom
11 blue	28 great	wise
able	grey	45 sword
deck	30 became	sharp
piece	33 rope	46 words
12 toot	car	48 read
13 listen	driver	(*past tense*)
speak	35 Japan	50 Arthur
India	sisters	51 bone
14 Captain	brothers	55 someone
Bob	37 presents	fallen
15 ahead		master
porpoise		

122

56 workmen	70 toes	100 flown
57 bark	slept	105 stairs
58 pump	71 sledge	hurry
59 everywhere	82 Johnnie	106 fares
61 goldfish	Appleseed	ladies
Richard	saucepan	109 crept
Granddad	America	113 gloves
62 jars	beautiful	Jill
65 fourth	83 already	pillar
fifth	84 hundreds	114 sorted
sixth	89 loved	116 without
66 seventh	90 part	write
67 pet	92 budgie	wrote
weed	Sandra	117 dustbin
68 room	else	118 dustmen
69 Eskimo	93 feathers	120 dustcart
puppy	thistledown	121 lucky
	95 teach	

OLIVER AND BOYD
Croythorn House,
23 Ravelston Terrace
Edinburgh EH4 3TJ
A Division of Longman Group Ltd.

First Published 1955
Second Edition 1963
Revised Edition 1971
Fifth Impression 1978

ISBN 0 05 002387 X

Printed in Hong Kong by
Wing King Tong Co Ltd,